The Very Young PIANIST

WORKBOOK A

by

Jane Smisor Bastien

GP 53

GENERAL WORDS & MUSIC CO., Publisher

ISBN 0-8497-6049-6

Unit 1
Alphabet Fill Ins

Think of the alphabet going UP on the keyboard and fill in the missing letters.

G	A	___	C	___	___	F
B	___	D	___	F	___	___
F	___	___	B	___	D	___

Think of the alphabet going DOWN on the keyboard and fill in the missing letters.

E	___	C	___	A	___	F
D	___	___	___	G	___	E
A	___	F	___	___	C	___

Naming Sharps

Write the letter names of the SHARPS which are colored on the keyboards.

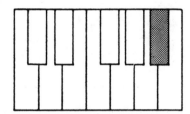 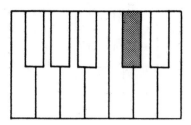 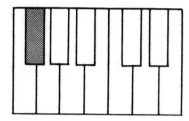

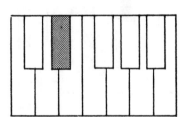 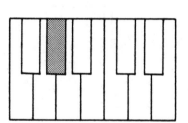 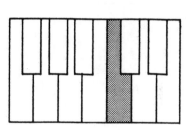

Color in the correct keys.

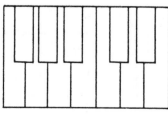 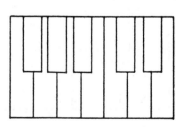 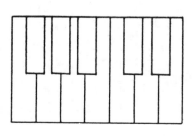

 F♯   C♯   G♯

Naming Flats

Write the letter names of the FLATS which are colored on the keyboards.

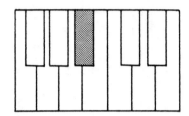

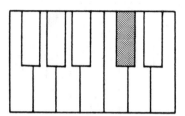

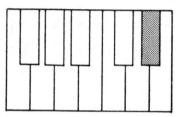

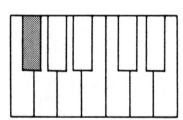

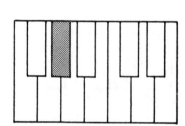

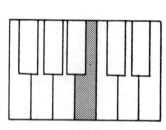

Color in the correct keys.

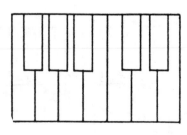

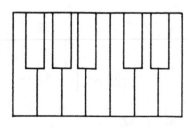

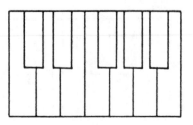

Db

Ab

Eb

Alphabet Fill Ins

Think of the alphabet going DOWN on the keyboard and fill in the missing letters.

A	___	___	E	___	C	___
G	___	___	D	___	B	___
B	___	G	___	E	___	C
C	___	___	G	___	E	___
E	___	C	___	A	___	F
D	___	B	___	___	F	___

Finding Sharps and Flats

Color in the correct keys below. Play these sharps and flats on the keyboard.

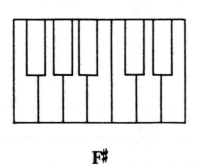

F♯

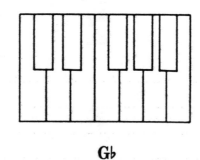

G♭

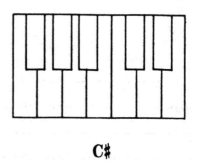

C♯

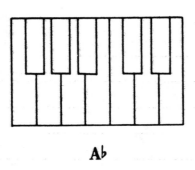

A♭

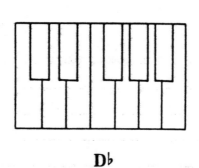

D♭

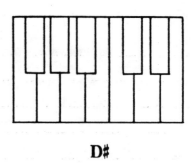

D♯

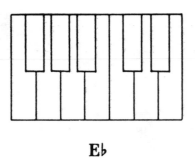

E♭

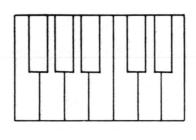

B♭

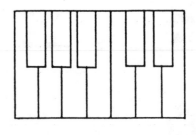

A♯

Alphabet Skips

Circle the alphabet skips below. Begin with the circled letters and skip UP or DOWN.

1. Skip UP

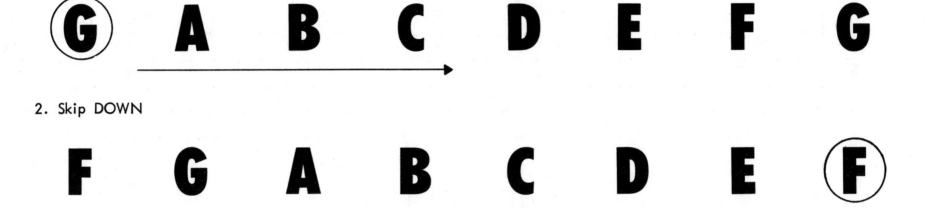

2. Skip DOWN

Write the letters which form alphabet skips DOWN from the given letters. Whisper the letter you skip when you see the question mark.

Five Finger Positions

Color the five keys in each of the positions below.

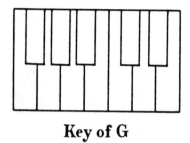

Key of G

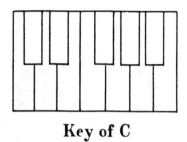

Key of C

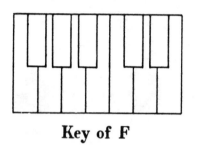

Key of F

Sharps and Flats

Color in the correct keys.

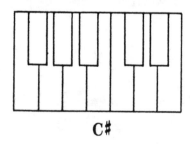

C#

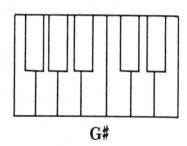

G#

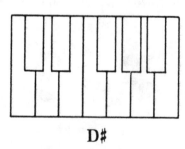

D#

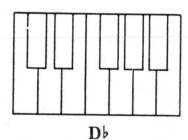

D♭

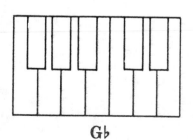

G♭

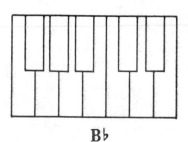

B♭

Recognizing Line and Space Notes

Color the LINE notes red and color the SPACE notes blue.

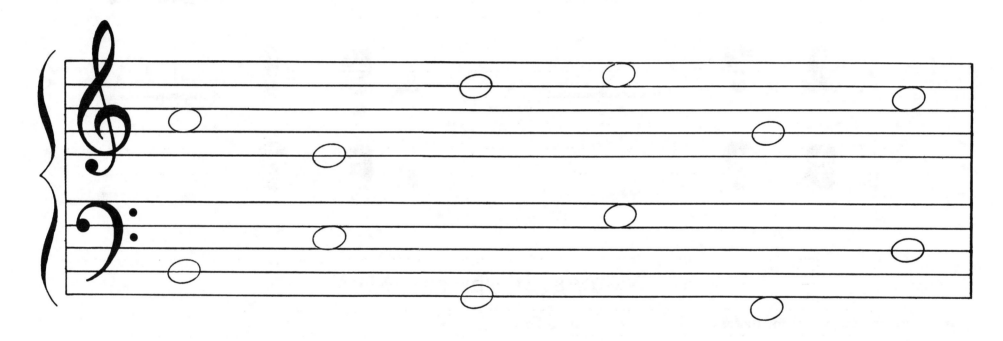

Draw some line and space notes.   Color the LINE notes red and color the SPACE notes blue.

Draw a
treble
clef

Alphabet Skips

Write the letters which form alphabet skips DOWN from the given letters. Whisper the letter you SKIP when you see the question mark.

1. **E ?** _____

2. **A ?** _____

3. **B ?** _____

4. **C ?** _____

5. **D ?** _____

6. **F ?** _____

Naming Sharps and Flats

Write the letter names of the sharps or flats colored on the keyboards.

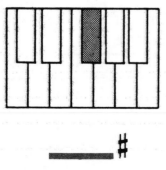

_____ #

_____ ♭

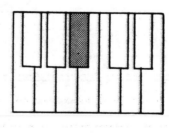

_____ #

_____ ♭

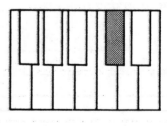

_____ #

_____ ♭

Drawing Skips

1. Draw skips UP from the given notes below.

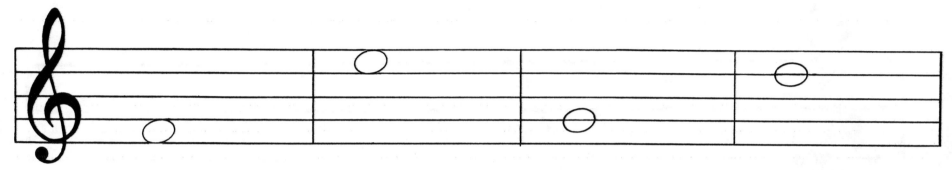

2. Draw skips DOWN from the given notes below.

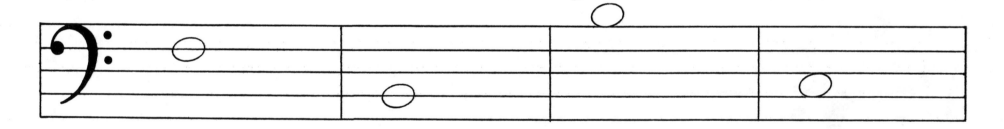

3. Draw skips either UP or DOWN from the given notes. Color the notes which form skips UP red; color the notes which form skips DOWN blue.

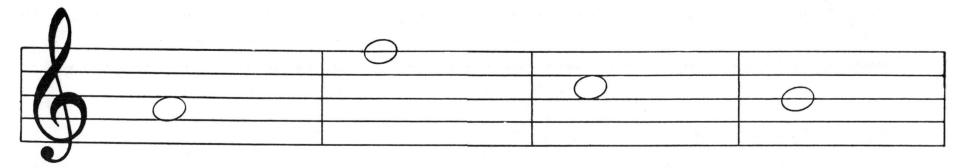

Naming the Lines

Beginning with bass line G, write the letter names of the LINE notes on the bass and treble staves.
*Always think by skips.

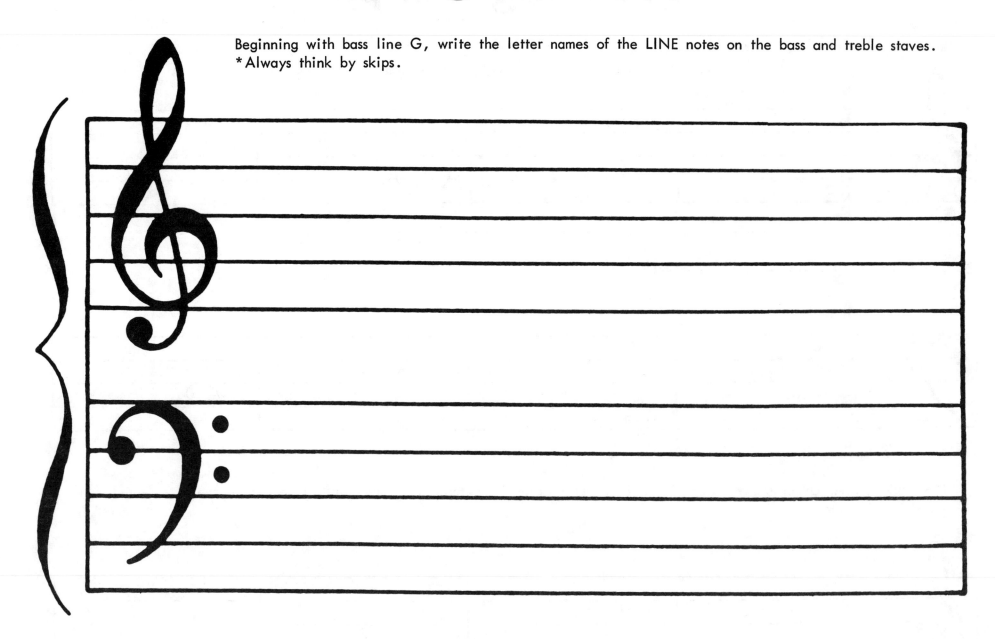

*For more practice, use the blank paper beginning on page 21.

Alphabet Skips

Write the letters which form alphabet skips UP from the given letters. Whisper the letter you skip when you see the question mark.

1. **C** **?** _____

2. **D** **?** _____

3. **A** **?** _____

4. **G** **?** _____

5. **F** **?** _____

6. **B** **?** _____

Write the letters which form alphabet skips DOWN from the given letters. Whisper the letter you skip when you see the question mark.

1. **B** **?** _____

2. **F** **?** _____

3. **A** **?** _____

4. **E** **?** _____

5. **C** **?** _____

6. **D** **?** _____

Recognizing Notes

Write the letter names of the notes on the blanks.

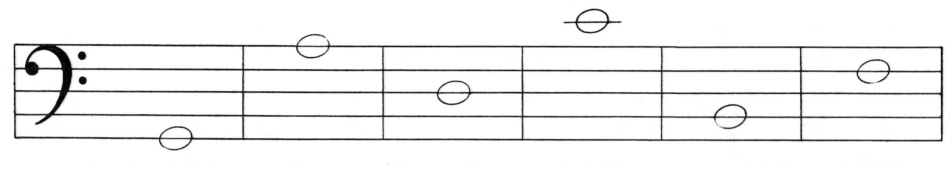

_____ _____ _____ _____ _____ _____

Draw the bass clef LINE notes below.

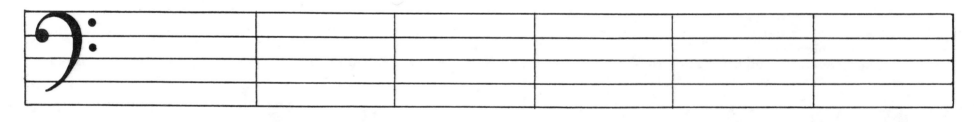

G   D   C   F   A   B

Sort out the bass clef LINE note flash cards and write the letter names of the notes on the blanks. Turn the cards over to check your answers.

1. _____   **2.** _____   **3.** _____   **4.** _____   **5.** _____   **6.** _____

Alphabet Steps

Write the letters which form alphabet steps UP from the given letters.

1. **B** ___ ___ ___ ___ ___

2. **D** ___ ___ ___ ___ ___

3. **F** ___ ___ ___ ___ ___

Write the letters which form alphabet steps DOWN from the given letters.

1. **G** ___ ___ ___ ___ ___

2. **F** ___ ___ ___ ___ ___

3. **C** ___ ___ ___ ___

Drawing Steps

1. Draw steps UP from the given notes below.

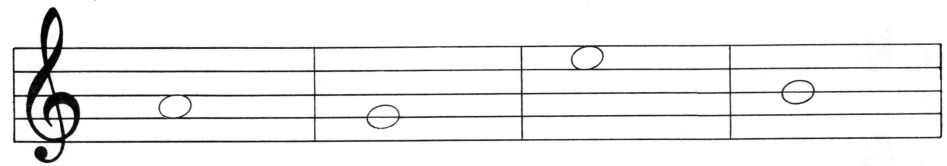

2. Draw steps DOWN from the given notes below.

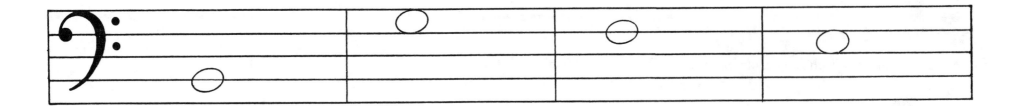

3. Draw steps either UP or DOWN from the given notes. Color the notes which form steps UP red; color the notes which form steps DOWN blue.

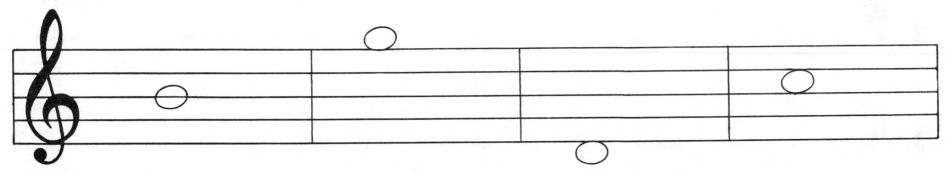

Recognizing Skips and Steps

Color the notes which form SKIPS red; color the notes which form STEPS blue.

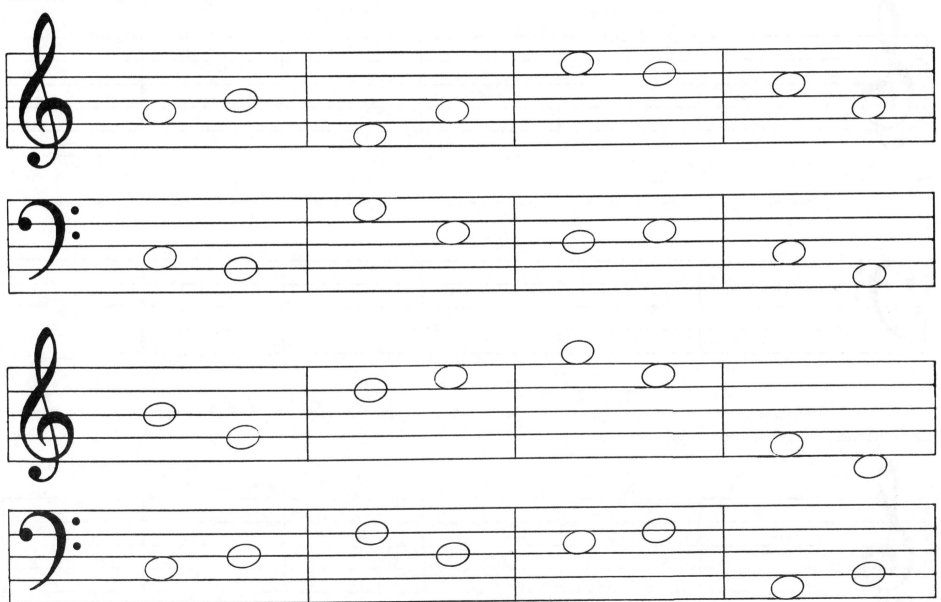

Naming Notes

Write the letter names of the notes on the blanks.

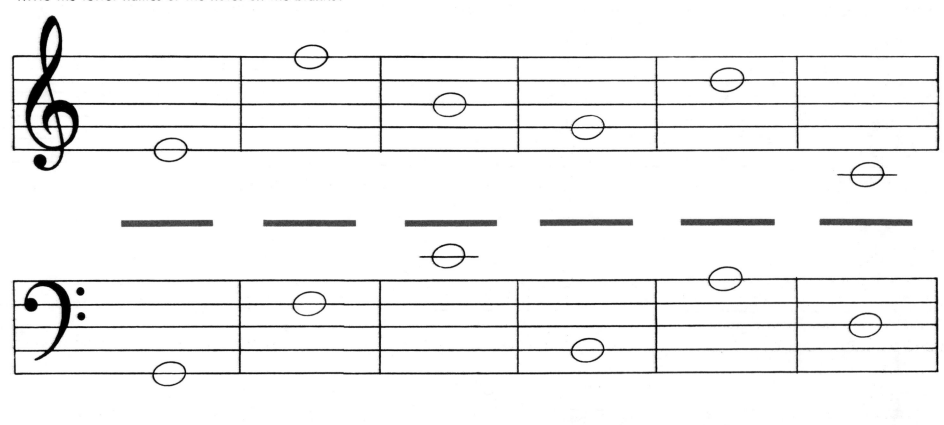

Draw the treble clef LINE notes below.

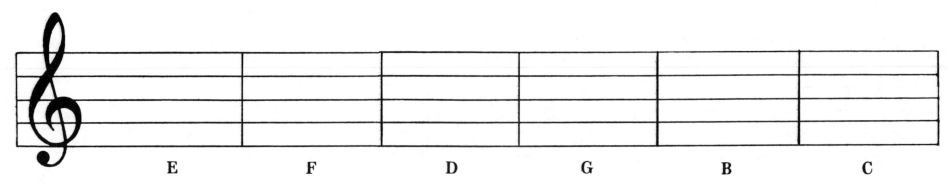

| E | F | D | G | B | C |

Naming the Spaces

Beginning with F below the bass staff, write the letter names of the SPACE notes on the bass and treble staves. Always think by skips.

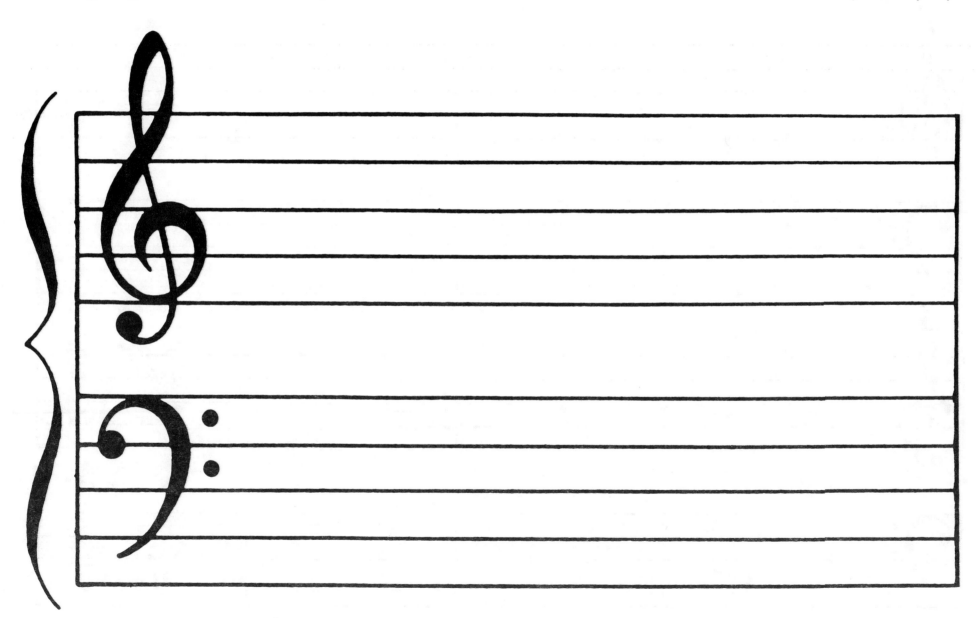

Recognizing Skips and Steps

Color the notes which form SKIPS red; color the notes which form STEPS blue.

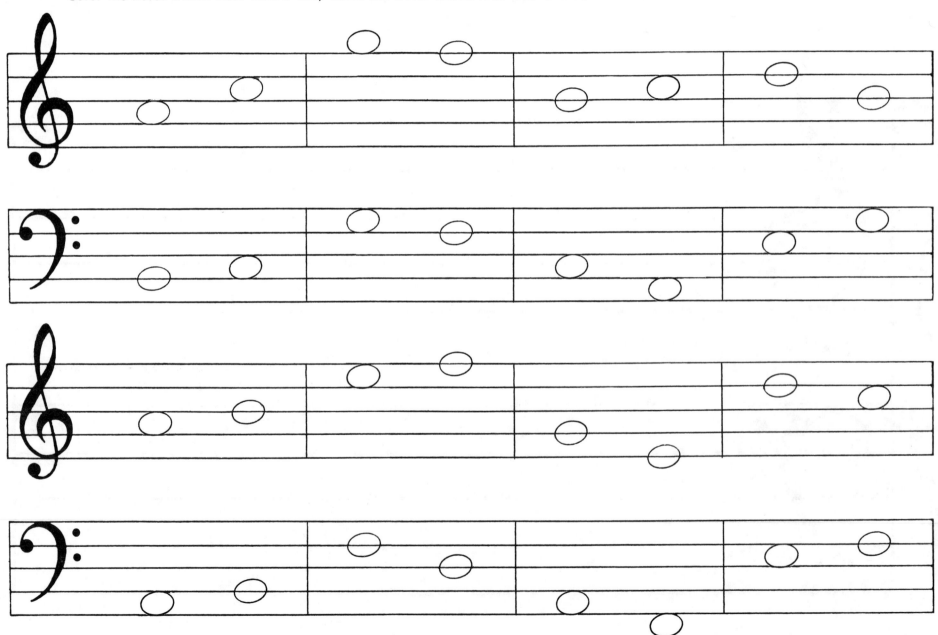